I'm Not a Pandacow

Monty
Dogge

M.T Sanders

Illustrations by Rebecca Sharp

First Edition published 2017 by 2QT Limited (Publishing) Settle, North Yorkshire BD24 9RH United Kingdom

Illustrations by Rebecca Sharp

Printed in Great Britain by Lightning Source

A CIP catalogue record for this book is available from the British Library

ISBN 978-1-912014-7-3

To my hoomans for keeping me in the manner to which
I've become accustomed especially poo bag who bent over
backwards for me (and sideways occasionally).
To the spangles for teaching me the real meaning of misery
and to all my friends on Facebook for having
too much time on their hands.
- Monty

To my family for the love and support
especially my beautiful wife Dawn
- Mark

For Dad, Christian and Leanne my family my life xx
- Rebecca

Imagine what it's like to share your meals with your ten brothers and sisters. Now imagine that those brothers and sisters are massive hairy puppies who climb on your head and push your face into your food. That was why I wasn't bothered about leaving for a new home today with these hoomans. They didn't look like they'd want my dinner ... at least I hoped not.

The other reason I didn't mind was that I'd met these hoomans before. They came to see me a few weeks ago. They picked me up and put me down, then picked me up and put me down again. I felt a bit sick but I thought it must be a new game. Today, though, I stayed picked up and I snuggled down with my new mum as I began the journey to wherever I was going.

After a long time in the car, we arrived. The first thing I noticed was how busy it was. There were hoomans and mini-hoomans. These were smaller versions of my new mum and dad and they seemed quite noisy. There were also other dogs, three of them, although it was hard to tell because they didn't stand still even for a second so counting them was quite difficult.

I had never seen anything like them before and, though they were a bit bigger than me, they ran around all the time making funny, squealing, excited noises.

They had mahoosive ears that flapped when they ran and I felt sure that at any moment they would take off.

I was placed on the floor and hooman Dad said, 'Everyone, this is Monty. Monty this is everyone' ... and that was the beginning of my new life.

I didn't speak to them straight away because I was so tired after my busy day and I just wanted to rest. Before I knew it, my eyes closed and I fell into a deep sleep. When I woke, everybody was still there so I thought it might be time to introduce myself properly to my new family.

They gathered round me and looked me up and down. 'What are you?' said Molly, who was the eldest of the three.

'I'm not sure,' I replied. 'Maybe I'm the same as you?' I wasn't sure that I was but I didn't want to seem silly. My ears were much smaller than theirs but maybe they'd grow.

'The same as us!' laughed Molly. 'The same as us ... ha! My dear boy, we are Cockeyed Spangles and whatever you are, you are NOT the same as us.'

Molly started singing a rhyme and the others joined in.

'You're not one of us, your ears are all wrong,
Yours are really short when they
should be long.

Dad says you're a dog but
I don't know how,
You look more
like a silly
Pandacow.'

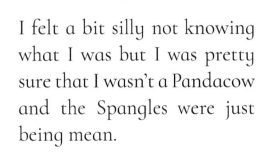

I felt a bit silly not knowing
what I was but I was pretty
sure that I wasn't a Pandacow
and the Spangles were just
being mean.

A strange thing happened over the next few weeks: the Spangles started getting smaller and smaller. Well, that's what I thought at first but then I realised that I was getting bigger … much bigger. After a few months I was five times bigger than the Spangles but, even though I had grown so large, they still teased me. I still didn't know what I was and they kept on calling me a Pandacow.

I really wanted to find out what I was and tried to think of how I could do it. Maybe, I thought, I could ask some of the other dogs I met on my walks. Surely somebody would know what I was. Maybe I'd even meet a dog just like me.

I met lots of other dogs when I was out so this should have been easy – or so I thought.

The first one I met was a fine looking black-and-white dog who was almost as big as me. I thought that maybe we could be the same.

'Hello, I'm Monty,' I said. 'I'm trying to find out what I am. Our coat is the same colour. Are you the same as me?'

The other dog looked me up and down then replied:

'I'm a Damnation, handsome and spotty.

You're black and white but you're pretty grotty.

I have a suggestion, I don't want a row,
But you look just like a Pandacow.'

And with that, he turned and walked away.

How rude was he? I was glad I was not the same as him.

The next dog I came across was another big dog and, although he wasn't the same colour as me, I asked anyway. He didn't seem impressed and replied:

'I am a snotwhiler,
I guard things and
look scary.

You look too friendly,
you're just big and hairy.

I'll have a guess,
if you will allow,
Maybe you are a Pandacow?'

We said goodbye and went our separate ways but I was starting to get worried ... was I really a Pandacow?

Around the corner came a small dog walking with its hooman. I thought maybe it was a pupster, so I asked if it would be the same as me when it grew up.

The small dog wasn't best pleased and replied angrily, 'I'm a Snack Rustle and this is the size I am meant to be!

'Down holes I chase, that's what I do.

You would get stuck, just look at you!

I don't have time for this right now,
See you later ... Pandacow.'

He sneered as he spoke. I'd obviously upset the little fella so I continued on my way.

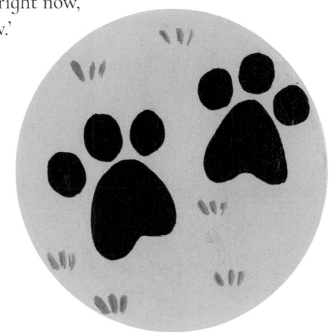

This was getting me nowhere and all I was doing was upsetting all the dogs I met. So, when a small black dog ran across the park towards me, I decided to be careful about what I said.

'Hello, small dog. You are very handsome. As you can see, I have a lot of black in my coat. Maybe we are long-lost brothers ... or cousins ... or just related?'

Well, the smaller dog looked me straight in the eye and laughed. 'Ha, ha, ha! Do you know what I am, laddie? I am a Scottyish Terror and you're no relative of mine.

'I'm proud and fearless and I'm a Scot.

Listen to you, you're clearly not.

I heard a rumour it could be true,
You look just like a Pandacoo.'

The Scottyish Terror was still laughing as he left. This day was not going too well at all.

Later on my walk, I came across a tall, slim dog. Being of similar size, I thought that if I went on a diet we could almost be the same. My hopes were dashed as the athletic-looking dog informed me that he was in fact a Greathound, and we were about as similar as ice cream and cornflakes.

'You can't run as fast as me,
You're not a Greathound anyone can see!

But if you'd like to race, we can do now,
I've never beaten a Pandacow.'

With that, the dog sprinted off at full speed and I realised he was right. Watching the Greathound zoom round the park made me feel out of breath. 'I'm certainly not one of them!'

Just when I was feeling fed up and sure I would never find out, I saw a dog in the distance that got me excited. We were similar in colour and both had rugged hair; the only difference was in our size.

As he got nearer, the other dog crouched down low. By the time he reached me, he was almost crawling on his stomach.

Thinking that being helpful was a good start to the conversation, I asked, 'Are you OK?' Do you need a paw up?'

He wasn't impressed that I didn't understand what he was doing. He was even less impressed when I asked if we could possibly be … the same.

'Firstly, there is nothing wrong with me. I am trained to do this. And secondly, NO, NO, NO! We are not even close to being the same.'

'I am Bored Old Collie and herding sheep is what I do,
They'd just laugh if they saw you.

You could maybe help pull the plough,
We haven't got a Pandacow.'

I couldn't help thinking he
was right and, to be honest,
I was quite pleased.
Chasing sheep and
crawling on my belly
didn't appeal to me at
all, nor did pulling a
plough ... whatever that
was.

A few weeks later, Dad took me out in the car. It was a long drive and after a while I fell into a deep sleep. When we stopped and Dad opened the door, I saw a huge lake in front of us. There was water as far as I could see and, just to one side, there was a group of hoomans with lots of dogs.

'Come on, Monts,' said Dad. 'You'll love this.' And he led me around the lake to where the others were playing.

As I got closer, I couldn't help but notice that all of the dogs were really big. In fact, they were all as big as me – and some were even the same colour.

They were swimming in the lake, playing with toys and a couple were even pulling hoomans along in the water, which looked a lot of fun.

I joined in but kept my distance because talking to other dogs didn't seem to go well for me.

Just before we were ready to leave, one of the other dogs came bouncing up to me and said, 'You did OK for your first time swimming.'

I was very proud that this magnificent dog thought that I'd done well and I thanked him.

'Er ... excuse me,' I said, not wanting to upset him. 'But what type of dog are you, if you don't mind me asking?'

The other dog let out a hooge loud bellowing laugh and said, 'Why, I'm the same as you! A Newfydoof, of course.' And with that, he turned and went back into the water.

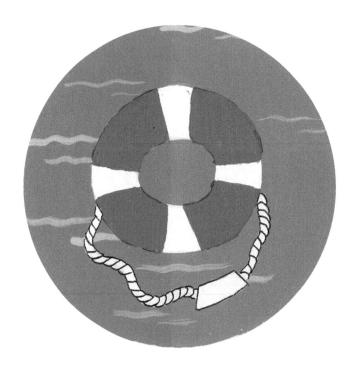

Back in the car, with the heater drying my fur, I looked through the window at all the Newfydoofs still playing in the lake.

'I'm a Newfydoof,' I thought, and I smiled the whole journey home. 'I can't wait to tell the Spangles. Wait until they hear how many other Newfydoofs I met.'